The Art of B
C

Chapters

as told to Cass Hollander
illustrated by Kristin Sorra

Harcourt

Orlando   Boston   Dallas   Chicago   San Diego

Visit *The Learning Site!*

www.harcourtschool.com

Introduction

I am a house cat. Let me begin by saying that this book is for house cats. If you want to live outdoors on your own, fending for yourself, there's no help for you. If you are wise, you will see the benefits of letting humans keep you safe and well fed. This book is your guide to a happy, satisfying life.

Humans often make the mistake of lumping cats and dogs together. As any cat knows, cats are nothing like dogs. A cat's disposition is completely different. It is our job to make being a cat an art. We must tutor humans in what we expect from them. This will stop them from trying to impose rules on us. We don't need rules from humans; we make our own rules.

The first thing to remember is that we cats choose the humans we want to live with. No matter what humans think, it is not the other way around. So, my cat reader, look for humans who are easy to train. Stay away from humans who are set in their ways. They will want to train you and make you fit into their lives.

HUMAN TEST

1. **Must own a large chair.**

2. **Must have NO other animals. (Especially DOGS!)**

3. **Must be trainable.**

4. **Must be willing to sit in one place for a very, very long time.**

Try this test. Go around and around the human's feet. What does the human do? If the human pushes you away irritably, you should leave fast. Such a human will never be a good cat companion. However, if the human reaches down to stroke your back, he or she shows real promise. Such a human could be perfect for you.

Life with Humans

We house cats differ from lions, tigers, and other big cats in one important way. They like to be on their own. House cats understand that it is better to live with humans.

When cats live with humans, the humans do the work. For example, the humans do the hunting. They provide the food. You will never have to lift a paw. Delicious cooked food will be given to you every day.

The danger is that you will like the food the humans provide too much. You might eat it happily whenever it is offered. This would be a mistake. You must keep the proper cat attitude toward food at all times. These are the house cat feeding rules.

RULE 1: Pick a time of day when you expect to be fed. This could be early morning or late afternoon. It could be the middle of the night. It is your choice.

RULE 2: When it is feeding time, demand your food. Walk around the kitchen, meowing and meowing. Walk in circles around your human. Meow and meow. If your human is asleep, you may have to take more drastic action. Poke the human with your paw. Meowing in the human's ear works, too.

RULE 3: Be picky about your food. Once in a while, turn up your nose and walk away. Let your human know that you are not easily satisfied and should not be taken for granted.

5

It's nice to have humans provide your food. However, some humans can get silly about giving you other things. You will have no use whatever for most of their gifts. Cat toys are good examples. Playing with a catnip mouse can be fun once in a while, but that's about it. A self-respecting cat should ignore other toys. Do not ever play with windup toys. Never engage in pastimes that make you look foolish.

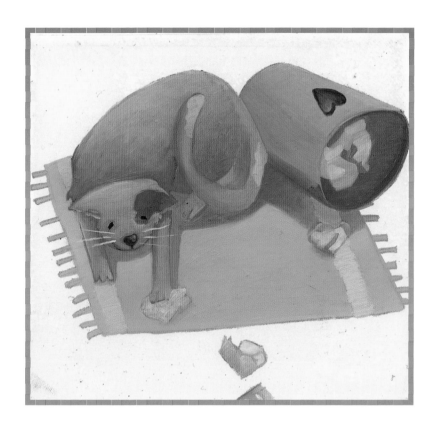

The truth is that cats don't need to be given toys. Any house is already full of them. Play with plants and flowers, spools of thread, and balls of string. Don't forget all the good stuff in wastebaskets! Be creative and make your own fun. Don't settle for the boring toys humans give you.

Another thing humans may give you is a scratching post. Never use it. Any of the following items are far better for making strong muscles and for sharpening your claws: rugs, carpeting, curtains, upholstered furniture, and your human's pant leg.

A cat bed is another thing that humans give cats. Some of these beds can be quite tempting. If you are given such a bed, you may lie in it only when your human cannot see you. When your human is at home, the best sleeping spots are any human clothing left on a chair, the back of a sofa, or the human's bed pillow.

Speaking of sleep brings up another subject. Be aware that humans like you to sit on their laps. Your regular human will behave glumly if you sit on someone else's lap. This can be fun for you. Choose someone who does not like cats. Be sure to jump up on strange humans as if you know them. Act as if you love them. Your human may be jealous, but most humans will not hold a grudge. In fact, your human will try even harder to please you.

Related to sitting on laps is the whole subject of petting. Humans think that pets love to be petted. They must have learned that from dogs.

They certainly didn't learn about petting from cats! When it comes to petting, it's important to have rules. You might want to have times when you allow petting. For example, you might permit petting during TV shows that star house cats. You may allow a little less petting during shows about lions, tigers, or cougars. Some house cats follow these rules with great success.

I have an "on demand" policy. Petting is allowed only when I demand it. I like to choose a time when the human's hands are busy doing something else. When I see my human drop everything to pet me, I know I've done a good training job.

More Words of Wisdom

Here are a few more important guidelines in the art of being a cat.

Taking a Bath

Washing is something we cats do for ourselves. As a cat, you must keep yourself clean at all times. This is important for your own well-being. However, your human may think you are not clean enough and may try to bathe you. You cannot allow that to happen. Never! Water is for drinking. It can even be fun to play with if it's dripping from a leaky faucet. However, you should never allow yourself to be put into water, to have it touch you and make your fur all wet. No way! Resist contact with water as if your life depends on it. Your self-esteem certainly does.

Travel

There are two kinds of travel a cat must deal with. The first is when the human goes somewhere and wants to take you along. The second is when the human goes somewhere but leaves you behind.

When the human wants to take you along, it can mean one of only two things. You are going to the vet, or you are moving. Both are things we cats would rather not do. So the minute you see the cat carrier coming out of the closet, hide. Stay out of reach. Your human will catch you after a while. When you are caught, struggle and hiss. When you are in the carrier, howl through the entire trip. This will make the trip so unpleasant that the human will never want to take you anywhere again.

Your human might think of going away and leaving you behind. Here's what to do if you think that's possible. Before the trip, when the human is packing, do everything you can to get in the way. Sit in the suitcase and knock things out of it. Hide wristwatches and keys. Play with socks and slippers.

Suppose the human goes anyway. When the human comes back from the trip, punishment is the rule. You should not have been left alone. You certainly should not have been put in a kennel. Pay no attention when you are being greeted. Humans like their pets to welcome them when they come home. Show your humans that if they wanted this kind of behavior, they should have gotten a dog.

Being Left Alone

As I explained in the previous rule, no human absence should ever go unpunished. Ignoring the human is the best punishment for long absences. For short absences, such as the time they spend at school or work, there are two possible punishments.

The first is to run around the house like crazy. Bounce off the furniture and the walls. This behavior scares humans. The second is to meow sadly at the door. This embarrasses them. Loud, sad meowing works especially well if you live in an apartment building where the neighbors can hear you. They will think your human has been mean to you.

Both these punishments must be used carefully. The idea is to make the human feel bad. If you overdo it, they may think you are lonely. You may find yourself having to share your home with another pet.

Noisy Machines

We expect humans to keep the house clean and tidy for us. That's not asking too much, is it? The problem comes when they start using those disgraceful robots to help them. Vacuum cleaners are enemy number one. Never attack one of these while it's on. Stay out of its way and hiss whenever you catch sight of it. When it's asleep and not looking, sneak up on it and bat it with your claws just to show it who's boss.

Companions

Humans often think that you would be happier if you had another pet to play with. This is not true, of course. The new pet may be another cat or, worse, a dog.

If another cat moves in, you and the new cat must bicker. Even if you know the new cat is nice, you must act up. You must not welcome any new pet. When the humans are away, you can hang out together, swap stories, and get to know each other. When the humans are there, however, you must hiss and spit and fight. Keep up this behavior for at least six months. That should be enough to discourage the human from bringing home any more cats.

Your humans may be unwise enough to bring a dog into the house. Don't panic. A dog is proof of your high standing as a cat. Humans who want dogs need the kind of love that a self-respecting cat would never give. Just be happy that nobody is expecting you to slobber all over him or her. You don't have to lie at the humans' feet and wag your tail. You don't have to act excited when the humans come home. In a household full of needy humans, a dog can take a lot of stress off a cat. Never be frightened by the huge size of some dogs. Remember this: "Cats rule. Dogs drool." We are the smarter animal. A small cat can push around a dog ten times its size.

So be true to yourself. Being a cat is an art. No other animal can be a house cat.